HURRICANE!

NATURE'S MOST DESTRUCTIVE FORCE

by Margo Sorenson

Perfection Learning® CA

For Jim, Jane, and Jill,
who were always willing to listen to "The Weather Woman."
For Ben, Joe, and Jak,
who eagerly read and commented on these ideas.
For Bonnie,
whose wise advice and sense of humor keeps all my writing on track.

Cover Illustration: Photo courtesy of American Red Cross
Inside Illustration: Kay Ewald

ABOUT THE AUTHOR

Margo Sorenson was born in Washington, D.C. She finished her school years in California, graduating from the University of California at Los Angeles. She taught high school and middle school and raised a family of two daughters while living in Hawaii for ten years. Mrs. Sorenson is now a full-time writer, writing primarily for young people junior high age and older.

Her years in Hawaii gave Mrs. Sorenson firsthand experience in living through hurricanes and near-hurricane force winds. She says that researching and writing this book was enjoyable because she learned much more about hurricanes than she knew when she actually lived through them. The research also reminded her of things she had forgotten about hurricanes. When she took science classes in school, she struggled to understand a lot of the concepts. Therefore, she decided to write this book so that students would be able to understand complex ideas in science more easily.

Mrs. Sorenson now lives in Minnesota with her husband, after having lived in Hawaii and California, but travels back to Hawaii almost every year. When she isn't writing books, she enjoys sports, watching the weather channel, and writing letters to her friends in Hawaii.

Text © 2005 by Perfection Learning® Corporation.
All rights reserved. No part of this book may be used or reproduced in any manner whatsoever without written permission from the publisher.
Printed in the United States of America. For information, contact
Perfection Learning® Corporation, 1000 North Second Avenue.
P.O. Box 500, Logan, Iowa 51546-1099.
Paperback ISBN 0-7891-6599-6
Cover Craft® ISBN 0-7569-4751-0
2 3 4 5 6 7 PP 11 10 09 08 07 06

Table of Contents

CHAPTER 1

THE RAGING WIND

"Hey! This is great, Damon!" The college student grinned at his friend.

"Didn't I tell you?" Damon smiled at Jeff.

The two boys stood on the balcony of a house that faced the ocean. Next to it, other houses dotted the shore. Condos and high-rises lined the coast as far as they could see.

"Right on the beach," Jeff said. "The whole weekend. Wait till the rest of the team gets here. Party time!"

"Yeah, my mom wasn't too happy about this trip," Damon said. He set his foot on the railing. He looked down at the sand below and sighed.

"No partying for her baby boy?" Jeff asked.

Damon frowned. "Nah. She's worried about the *hurricane watch*." Damon traced spirals on the railing with his finger.

Both boys looked up at the blue sky. It was clear except for little wispy clouds. And they looked innocent enough.

"Oh, was that it?" Jeff snickered. "There are always hurricane watches here in Florida."

"Yeah, you're right," Damon said. "But this is even bigger than usual. And Mom always worries." He flicked some sand off the railing with his finger.

Damon looked back up at the clouds. It didn't look like a hurricane was coming. Wouldn't the sky be threatening? Wouldn't there be black, ugly clouds? Wouldn't the wind be whistling in their ears?

Then Damon looked out at the ocean. It looked peaceful enough. There weren't any whitecaps. No surf was pounding the sand. It was just the end of another beautiful day on the Florida coast. His mom just worried too much.

"Bigger than usual? That's what they always say," Jeff said. He grinned at Damon. "Those weather guys don't know anything. Think of all the hurricane watches we've had. Nothing ever happens.

"Just wait till the chicks hit the beach tomorrow." He looked at Damon and wiggled his eyebrows. "That'll make you feel better."

Damon's mood brightened. "Yeah, that'll be great. And we'll have a great view from here!"

In front of them, the Atlantic Ocean curled up onto the beach. The waves lapped the shore. The soft wind blew on their faces. The setting sun shone behind them and warmed their backs.

How could anyone worry about a hurricane with this beautiful weather? Damon wondered. Jeff was right. The weather forecasters never knew what they were talking about.

"I'm sure glad Mom's friend took pity on two poor college students," Damon said. "She figured we could use a break from studying."

Jeff laughed. "What studying?" He elbowed Damon.

"Yeah, yeah, yeah," Damon said. "Whew," he added. He took off his shirt. "Don't you think it's kinda muggy?" He frowned out at the ocean. "You'd think with the breeze, it wouldn't feel this humid."

"You've been in the classroom too long," Jeff joked. "Gotta

 6

get you out into the real world."

Jeff looked up and down the beach. "Yeah. The rest of the team is gonna love this."

"Let's unpack the groceries," Damon said. He turned to go inside. Then he looked back over his shoulder at the sky. It looked fine to him. So why did he feel a growing sense of doom in the air?

Damon shook his head. He had to stop worrying. He was getting as bad as his mom. Everyone else would think he was a wimp for sure.

The boys went inside and unpacked. Then they went out for a hamburger.

At the restaurant, everyone was talking about the hurricane watch.

"I'm going right to the store," one woman said. "I've got to get batteries."

"I need bottled water," another woman said.

"Maybe we should just get out of town," a man added.

"No," a second man scoffed. "These weather forecasters don't know nothin'."

"See?" Jeff whispered to Damon. But Damon was staring at the TV on the wall.

A weatherman was rattling on about hurricanes. Huge blue and white swirls filled the screen behind him. Damon heard the words "might be a force-four hurricane. Wind speeds up to 155 miles per hour."

Damon felt uneasy. He looked over at Jeff and started to say something. But then he stopped. No sense in having Jeff think he was a coward.

On the drive home, Damon flicked on the radio. The announcer's voice blared in his ears.

Repeat. People in low-lying coastal areas should prepare to

evacuate. Hurricane Warren headed straight for the Florida coast. Repeat.

Damon glanced at Jeff from the corner of his eye. Jeff sighed in disgust and flipped the dial to another station. Music poured into the car.

When they got back to the house, there was a message on the answering machine. It was Damon's mom.

"I'm concerned about the *hurricane warnings,*" she said. She sounded really worried. "Please give me a call, Damon."

Damon looked across the room at Jeff. Jeff lolled on the couch, clicking the TV remote back and forth.

I'll call her back tomorrow, Damon thought. He walked outside. The air was really wet and sticky. Up above, the sky had changed. The clouds were fatter. They were lower too.

Damon stared out at the ocean. The tide was coming in, faster and stronger than before.

Were the waves always this high? Were they coming in higher than an hour ago? Were they going to sweep the house away in the night?

In spite of the heat, a shiver ran down his spine. Knock it off, bud, Damon told himself angrily. Get a grip.

Just then, Damon felt a raindrop. Then another. And another. Then rain began pelting him.

He ran inside and slammed the sliding door behind him. "Hey, Jeff," he said. "It's starting to rain. Maybe this hurricane thing is real."

Jeff didn't even look up. "Sheesh. I can't get anything except this dumb hurricane news," he complained. Damon felt a chill of fear.

Jeff looked over at Damon. "But they're not talking about any hurricanes for around here," he went on.

"Besides," Jeff said with a grin, "we'll just have a hurricane party. We'll hole up with drinks and food and watch everything blow away. It'll be cool."

It doesn't sound too cool to me, Damon thought.

Just then the phone rang. Damon hurried to answer it. It was his mom's friend, Bernice.

"Take all the furniture in from the balcony," she directed. "There's duct tape in the bottom kitchen drawer. Seal the windows and doors with it. Then use it to make big x's across the windows. I wish I had bought storm shutters," she added.

She paused, thinking. "There are flashlights and batteries next to the sink. Bottled water is under the sink."

Her worried voice halted again. "You should be all right," she said. "I'd tell you to evacuate, but these forecasters are never right. And the house is well built. Thanks for looking after it."

Jeff just grinned as Damon began working. Eventually, he did help a little, but he complained loudly.

"All this for nothin'," Jeff grumbled, carrying in a chair from the balcony. He shook his head. "Dumb hurricane." Then he grinned. "But it'll be a great party!"

Damon looked out before he went to bed. The wind had picked up. Sand pelted the windows facing the ocean. Trash-can lids banged and clattered along the curbs. A lawn chair thwacked into the house next door.

He stared out at the ocean. The surf crashed loudly. The incoming tide covered yards and yards of beach. It looked as if the waves were almost up to the house.

Damon walked out onto the balcony. The blowing sand stung his skin. He couldn't see. He rushed back inside.

That night, Damon tossed and turned in bed. Outside, the wind whistled viciously. He had never heard anything like it. It

 **9**

sounded as if it would pick the roof right up off the house.

The house creaked and shook. Good thing the house stood high above the sand on pilings. But would that be enough? Would it save them?

WHACK! Damon sat up in bed. What was that? It sounded like something had hit the house—something big! Had a car run into the house? He rushed out of his bedroom.

Jeff was standing in the hall, looking sleepy. Damon flicked on the light. "What was that?" Damon asked.

"I dunno," Jeff answered. They headed toward a window.

Just outside the window, a patio table lay on the ground in pieces.

"Jeez," Damon said. "Some dumb jerk didn't take his stuff inside. Good thing that table didn't hit a window!"

Just then, the lights went out. "Oh, great," Damon said. He felt his way to the kitchen and found a flashlight.

The light played eerily on his face and threw shadows on the wall. The wind whined and shook the house. The wind almost seemed alive. Was it trying to force its way inside?

The windows rattled in their frames. Rain sheeted and gusted against the windows. It sounded like bullets. Damon was sure the glass would break with the force of the rain.

Then he heard loud, dripping noises. He shone his flashlight on the windows. Pools of water were forming on the floor.

"Look at that," Damon said. He showed Jeff the dripping water. "If the surf doesn't get us, the rain will," he said.

THUD! The house shook. A ripping, splintering sound filled the air. Damon froze. "What happened?" he yelled above the noise of the wind.

Jeff's face drained of color. "I dunno," he said.

"It sounded like a tree or something," Damon said. "It must have fallen on our roof."

Damon gripped the flashlight. "What do we do now?" he asked. "If it crashed through the roof, the roof might go."

He stared at Jeff. Jeff's face was shadowed, but his eyes were wide with fright. Some hurricane party, Damon thought.

CRASH! A huge wave crashed right on the balcony. Foam splashed up against the front windows. They rattled with the force of the water. Damon heard the splintering and cracking of wood. The balcony was gone, he realized. The wave had ripped it right off the house.

"Should we get in the car?" Jeff screamed above the roar of the wind and the water.

"We'd never make it," Damon yelled back. "We can't go outside in this. We'd blow away. Everything's all flooded outside too."

Damon tried to remember about hurricanes. What should they do about the roof? Where could they hide?

Then he remembered. They had to get to a room with no windows. But where? A closet?

That was it. They'd get into a closet. If the roof was going to go, that might help. Then they'd pray the door wouldn't be blown off.

"A closet," Damon hollered above the wind. "We need to get in a closet."

Damon grabbed a stool. Jeff followed. They squished into the hall closet. Damon slammed the door shut. Then he wedged the stool under the handle.

The house shook and groaned. Suddenly, a huge wrenching sound ripped through the air. The house shook violently. "The roof! It got the roof!" Damon yelled.

Just then, a gigantic wave slammed into the house. It twisted the closet door right off its hinges. A wall of water crashed into the closet.

 **11**

"Noooooo!" Jeff screamed. He gurgled and choked. He disappeared into the frothing water.

Damon grabbed for Jeff's hand. But an invisible force sucked it beneath the surging waves.

That was the last thing Damon heard his friend say. That was the last thing he heard anyone say. A roaring in his ears blocked out everything.

There would be no hurricane party after all.

American Red Cross

 **12**

CHAPTER

SEEDS OF DESTRUCTION

What is a hurricane?

Rains that drench. Winds that destroy. A *storm surge* that kills. Destruction everywhere.

Why do people fear hurricanes so much? Aren't earthquakes worse? Or *tsunamis?*

The answer is no. Hurricanes are the most destructive force in nature—nature's most powerful machine. Since 1900, hurricanes have killed more people than earthquakes. They cause billions of dollars in damage. They bring more suffering than any other natural disaster.

Most people think hurricanes are just high winds. But they are much more than wind.

A hurricane creates its own power. It feeds itself. It is like a giant spinning top made of extreme winds and rain clouds. It spins under its own power—a wind system out of control.

Hurricanes have several names. But they're all the same disastrous wind systems.

When these wind systems form over the Atlantic Ocean, they're called *hurricanes*. The name comes from the Central American word *urican*, meaning "god of stormy weather."

 13

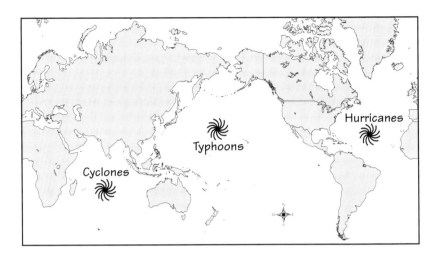

Over the Pacific Ocean, they're named **typhoons.** This comes from the Chinese word *taifeng.*

In the Indian Ocean, people call them **cyclones.** But they all work the same way. They bring the same death and destruction.

How is a hurricane different from a regular storm?

There are many differences between a hurricane and a regular storm. Winds in a hurricane spin and rotate. They move in a circular motion at a high rate of speed. Regular storm winds don't spin.

Another difference is the wind speed. Hurricane winds are much faster than storm winds.

- A tropical cyclone with winds of up to 38 mph is called a *tropical* **depression.**
- One with winds of 39–73 mph is a *tropical storm.*
- When winds reach 74 mph or more, the storm is called a hurricane.

Also, a hurricane rips across the landscape with much more power than a regular storm. Energy in an ordinary storm could light the whole United States for 20 minutes. But the power in a hurricane is 12,000 times that strong.

 **14**

Think of the untold human suffering and agony such power can cause. The hurricane in Bangladesh in 1991 killed over 250,000 people.

Hurricanes are also much larger than storms. A hurricane can measure from 200 to 600 miles across.

What does a hurricane look like?

A hurricane is a giant *whirlpool* of winds. The clouds on top can reach to 40,000 or 50,000 feet. They look like an enormous thundercloud.

In satellite photographs, hurricanes look like a solid cloud mass. But they are really made up of rings or bands of intense thunderstorms.

In the center lies the calm *"eye" of the hurricane.* The eye can measure about 20 miles across. Inside it are light winds and mild weather.

Dark center shows eye of Hurricane Hugo in this colorized satellite image from the NOAA.

Within the rest of the hurricane, raging winds blow up to 200 mph. Rain pounds down from the cloud wall around the eye. Bands of rain fill the rest of the hurricane.

Few people have survived the full power of a hurricane. There is no truly safe shelter. The wind speeds are too dangerous.

For example, at 125 mph, a straw can be driven right through a wooden plank. Imagine what happens to buildings— or people—in that wind.

How do winds cause hurricanes?

Several factors create hurricanes. Wind patterns are a factor.

Warm air and cold air move. When they move, they change the weather.

Warm air rises. It's lighter than cold air. Cold air sinks. It's heavier than warm air. These movements cause wind. It's amazing to think that something as simple as rising and falling air could create such danger.

Heat drives the wind cycle. The sun is hottest at the *equator,* so there's lots of warm air there. This warm air is always rising at the equator.

Where warm air is rising, it isn't pushing so hard against the earth. We call this a ***low pressure area.*** And when the warm air rises, cooler air pours in to fill the low pressure area.

Something else is happening at the same time. At the poles, the sun's rays don't heat the air as well. So the air is cold.

The cold air keeps sinking, pushing against the earth. Where cold, heavy air is slowly sinking to the earth, it forms a ***high pressure area.*** Air moves from the high pressure area to the low pressure area.

Movements of air from high pressure areas to low pressure areas are winds. This cycle of moving air helps create a hurricane.

 16

The spinning motion of the earth changes the wind patterns. The winds don't blow straight from the North Pole to the equator. They don't blow straight from the South Pole to the equator.

The earth's spinning makes the winds bend. This is called the **Coriolis effect.** At the equator, winds blow almost parallel to the equator. In the *northern hemisphere,* they bend clockwise. In the *southern hemisphere,* they bend counterclockwise.

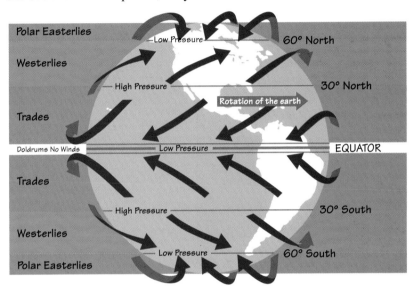

The Coriolis effect influences how a hurricane travels. That's why it's so hard to tell where a hurricane might hit. It also makes hurricanes more powerful and dangerous.

First, the cold air sinks. It begins flowing toward the equator—the low pressure areas. Then, it warms up again. It rises as it flows up and back to its pole.

Think of it as two huge conveyor belts—the northern hemisphere and the southern hemisphere. The belts carry the winds from low to high and back to low again.

But the Coriolis effect changes this flow of air. The earth spins at over 620 mph at the equator. This spinning makes the two basic belts in each hemisphere break up into three belts.

 **17**

The winds now blow in opposite directions in each of the three belts. This makes it easier for hurricanes to form.

The three belts in each hemisphere are called *convection cells*. The first cells in each hemisphere, around the poles, are the smallest. The next ones are bigger. They circle the earth a little lower. The last and largest cells lie right next to the equator in both hemispheres.

The wind system on the earth acts like a giant air conditioner. It helps keep the earth's surface cool by causing the warm air to rise away from the earth. But it also makes perfect wind conditions for hurricanes.

How hard does the wind blow in a hurricane?

The *Beaufort Scale* shows wind strength. On this scale, hurricane force is force 12. That means the wind speed is at least 75 mph.

BEAUFORT SCALE

AVERAGE FORCE	AVERAGE SPEED (MPH)	EFFECTS
1	2	smoke drifts
2	6	leaves rustle
3	10	twigs move
4	16	small branches move
5	22	small trees sway
6	28	large branches move
7	35	whole trees move
8	43	small branches break
9	50	houses damaged slightly
10	59	trees broken
11	70	widespread damage
12	75+	destruction

Now you can see how much damage a hurricane can cause. Remember, a storm isn't a hurricane unless it has winds of over 75 mph.

 **18**

What else besides wind is needed to make hurricanes?

Besides wind, nature needs water and heat to make hurricanes. Water and heat provide the energy for the winds.

Air is made up of many different kinds of molecules. Some of them are molecules of water called **water vapor.**

Evaporation from the ocean makes most of the water vapor in the air. Ocean water absorbs heat from the sun. When a water droplet has enough heat energy, it breaks away from the liquid. At the same time, warm air is rising. So the water becomes water vapor—tiny, tiny droplets of water that mix with the warm, rising air.

As the water vapor rises, it cools. Finally, it gets cold enough. Then it condenses into droplets of liquid water again. These droplets form clouds. While they are condensing into clouds, the droplets release most of their heat energy received from the sun.

If you've ever blown breath on a cold window, you have done the same thing. The tiny water droplets in the air from your mouth cool when they hit the window. They cloud the window.

 19

The heat energy from these water droplets helps power the hurricane. Hard to believe, isn't it? How can a huge destructive force like a hurricane run on energy from water droplets?

Water evaporates all the time from the seas and oceans. Think of how much water that is. Think of the billions of water droplets rising. This process releases heat energy constantly.

People never notice the tremendous power of this heat energy until a hurricane forms. The total energy released by a hurricane each day is the same as that of a billion tons of flaming fuel. It is the same as several hundred 20-megaton hydrogen bombs.

Where do hurricanes begin?

Most scientists agree that hurricanes form over water that is at least 78 degrees. So they don't form in latitudes higher than 30 degrees from the equator. The water is too cold.

And they can't form from zero to ten degrees north—right around the equator. There the air is almost vertical. So there isn't enough wind.

Remember the Coriolis effect? The air moves parallel to the equator. And hurricanes need winds to help evaporate seawater. If there's no wind, there's no hurricane.

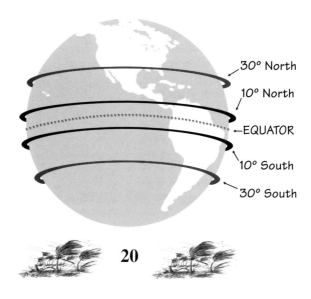

30° North
10° North
←EQUATOR
10° South
30° South

How do hurricanes form?

Hurricanes begin with a "disturbance" of some kind. Most Atlantic hurricanes begin with a low pressure center. This center may have started as a West African thunderstorm. It moves west.

Scientists find that the amount of rain in West Africa affects how many hurricanes develop. You'll learn more about this in chapter 5.

There has to be a mix of the right wind and temperature pattern. When the right pattern exists, the very moist air above the warm water begins to be drawn up.

Remember, warm, moist air rises. It becomes cooler as it rises. Then the water vapor condenses into clouds and rain. This *condensation* releases lots of energy.

When this energy is released, *updrafts* carry water vapor and heat still higher. This upward pull of air creates a deep low pressure area at the surface. Winds begin to be sucked into this low pressure system. The wind rushes in to fill a low pressure area.

Then the Coriolis effect makes these winds begin to spin. The stronger the air current rising, the tighter the swirl of winds. If the pressure keeps dropping, the winds get even stronger.

The storm forms an eye surrounded by a towering wall of clouds. This is called the **eye wall.** Here the strongest band of wind and rain is found. In the strongest hurricanes, this is like a gigantic tornado.

This eye-wall band rages with the most destruction. A fully developed hurricane pumps out about two million tons of air per second. This results in more rain in one day than falls in New York City in a year. During Hurricane Andrew, which rammed into Florida in 1992 (see chapter 4), the winds blew at more than 160 mph.

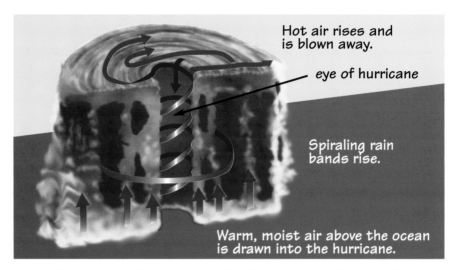

Hot air rises and is blown away.

eye of hurricane

Spiraling rain bands rise.

Warm, moist air above the ocean is drawn into the hurricane.

The eye-wall band is powerful. Strong upper-level winds there act as exhaust fans. They pipe away the hot air rising within the storm. Every second, maybe a million tons of warm air shoot up through the hot towers in the eye wall.

As hot air is blown away, more warm, moist air is sucked in at the bottom. This provides even more energy for the storm. The storm gets stronger.

Rain bands are lines of intense rain clouds and high winds. They circle inside the hurricane around the eye wall. Next to them are lighter clouds and winds. Then another rain band follows.

Because of this, hurricanes don't bring steady rain. Instead, periods of hard rain and wind follow periods of lighter rain and wind. Each rain band takes its turn pounding the earth below.

The whole hurricane rages. It moves forward at about 10 to 30 mph. When it gets over land or cooler water, it dies—cut off from its fuel of warm water.

But it is when the hurricane slams into land that it causes the most damage. The hurricane brings not only powerful winds, but also huge waves called storm surges.

The destruction is just beginning.

HURRICANE FURY

How can we know when to get ready for a hurricane?

How do hurricanes move? What are their paths? When will they come?

Hurricanes are big and dangerous. We should be able to tell where they're going. We should know when they're coming. But we don't.

It's hard to tell where a hurricane will hit. They seem to move randomly. They can even spin in loops upon loops.

Hurricanes are a weather forecaster's nightmare. There are many different wind systems that can change a hurricane's path. They steer the hurricane in new directions.

In the Atlantic Ocean, the winds sweep hurricanes to the west. The hurricanes can rip into the southern coast of the United States. Or sometimes they threaten the mid-Atlantic and New England states.

In the Pacific Ocean, hurricanes usually move north or northwest. But once in a while, they move northeast. Then they rage onto the west coast of Mexico.

If hurricanes travel too far north, the cold ocean water off the west coast of the U.S. will weaken them.

Hurricanes seldom reach the West Coast as tropical storms. They also rarely hit Hawaii. Just six hurricanes have threatened Hawaii between 1950 and 1992. Hurricane Iniki, which nearly wiped out Kauai in 1992, was rare.

Hurricanes usually travel at about 12–16 mph. The slower the speed of the storm, the worse the effect. That's because the winds have more time to cause damage.

So are fast-moving hurricanes less destructive? Not really.

Sometimes stronger middle-latitude winds steer hurricanes. Then they speed up to 25–50 mph. This shortens the warning time for people to evacuate. The population has no time to prepare.

What is the weather like just before a hurricane hits?

On the day before, the weather is usually very good. There are only a few clouds. Late in the afternoon, high-level clouds begin to blow in. And the air feels muggy.

Several hours later, lower, thicker clouds follow these high clouds. Showers begin. They increase. They get heavier. The wind begins to blow hard.

Finally, a dark wall of clouds approaches. The full fury of the hurricane unleashes.

But the fury isn't steady. Remember the rain bands? Periods of extreme violence take place. Then periods of lighter wind and rain follow them. Then the hard rain and wind come again.

What happens when a hurricane slams into shore?

When a hurricane hits land, it causes destruction in three ways: wind, rainfall, and storm surge. Hurricane winds are very strong. The strength of the hurricane depends on the speed of the wind.

24

Scientists have a scale for judging hurricane strength. Robert Simpson, director of the *National Hurricane Center,* and Herbert Saffir, a consulting engineer, devised the *Saffir-Simpson scale.* It is used all over the world.

SAFFIR-SIMPSON SCALE

	WIND SPEEDS (MPH)	STORM SURGE (FEET)	DAMAGE
Force 1	74–95	4–5	Minimal
Force 2	96–110	6–8	Moderate
Force 3	111–130	9–12	Extensive
Force 4	131–155	13–18	Extreme
Force 5	156+	19+	Catastrophic

As the wind speed increases, the storm surge and damage increase. But a 40-mph wind isn't just twice as strong as a 20-mph wind. There is a math formula to figure wind force. The increase in wind force equals the square of the increase in wind speed.

In other words, if the wind speed doubles, the force of the wind increases by 4 *(2^2)*. So a 40-mph wind is 4 times as destructive as a 20-mph wind. And a 60-mph wind is 9 times *(3^2)* as powerful as a 20-mph wind.

Hurricane winds are unique. Not only are they strong, but they blow in gusts. They don't blow steadily. And things rip apart more easily in gusty winds.

It's easy to see how hurricane winds can destroy so much. Branches break and trees are uprooted. Bushes are blown flat. Houses and buildings are destroyed. Shingles, even whole roofs, blow off. Windows and doors are blown out. Chimneys blow over. Walls blow over. Wooden buildings blow away completely.

And everything blown loose becomes like a huge bullet. Doors blown off someone's house can slam into another house.

Besides the wind, hurricanes bring torrential rain. Rain pounds the landscape. Streams and rivers swell with extra rainwater. They can wash soil and plants away.

Hurricanes have brought some of the world's heaviest rainfalls. In 1911, one hurricane poured 88 inches of rain on the Philippines. That is almost the total annual rainfall for the island of Guam.

It's hard to know exactly how much rain falls during a hurricane. The wind blows so hard that the rain gauges can't even collect all the rain. Wind whips a lot of the rain almost parallel to the ground. In winds over 52 mph, rain gauges collect only about 50 percent of the rain.

One of the deadliest parts of a hurricane is the storm surge. Storm surge causes nine out of ten hurricane deaths and much property damage.

As the hurricane moves over the ocean, the surface water is drawn into the storm's low pressure area. Remember how air flows into low pressure areas? Water does the same.

 26

A huge bulge of water forms beneath the hurricane's eye. The mound of water may be 50 miles wide. It rises about a foot or so above the rest of the ocean. Then deep ocean currents carry it to the land.

Giant waves begin roaring into shore. As the water gets more shallow, the mound of water has nowhere to go but up. Then the wind whips the massive waves onto the coast. Storm tides 15 feet higher than normal wash over the land. They can sweep ashore 50–100 miles inland.

Strong hurricane winds blow across the top of the water too. This makes giant waves 5–10 feet high or higher. These are on top of the already high storm surge.

The terrible surge and the higher waves rage ashore. They rake over everything in their paths.

Storm surges don't stop at the coastline. They grow higher and more dangerous if they're forced up a narrow channel. Hurricanes also cause huge floods inland as they release the tons of water they've been carrying.

National Weather Service

It's easy to see why storm surges are so deadly. In Hurricane Camille in 1969, storm surges of 15–20 feet slammed into the coast.

One cubic yard of water weighs 3/4 of a ton. Imagine tons and tons of water smashing onto the shore. Storm surges killed 6,000 people in the 1900 hurricane in Galveston, Texas.

How do scientists study hurricanes?

A hurricane is truly an engine of death and destruction. People hope that learning about them will help save lives and property.

One of the first people to study hurricanes was Father Benito Vines. He was named the "hurricane priest." He set up a lab in Cuba in 1870. Ship captains reported hurricanes at sea to him. He also had volunteer watchers all along the Cuban coastline.

But ships had to reach land before they could report seeing a storm. Then Father Vines did his best to warn others. At that time, warnings were slow.

When the wireless telegraph was invented, warnings got quicker. Ships could wire information as soon as they saw a storm.

Today, there are three ways scientists track hurricanes.

Air

In the early days, scientists sent up weather balloons. The balloons carried instruments to measure conditions in the atmosphere. These are helpful today, but it is not always easy to get them back.

No one had seen a hurricane from the air until 1943. That was the year Colonel Joseph Duckworth flew his plane right through a hurricane.

 28

Duckworth opened up a whole new way to track and forecast hurricanes. For the first time, people had data and readings from inside the hurricane.

The airplane, though, can patrol a huge area of the ocean. In the 1940s, the U.S. Navy began flying regular air patrols to track hurricanes. The air patrols give warnings and report the progress of hurricanes as they travel.

Today's planes, the "hurricane hunters," are flying labs. They have computers and weather instruments. Most *meteorologists* believe that hurricane aircraft patrols get data that can't be found any other way.

Satellite

The satellite plays a big role in hurricane tracking. First, the aircraft computers collect the data. Then they bounce it off a satellite. The data feeds into computers at the National Hurricane Center.

Meteorologists study this data. Then they make predictions. They judge when and where the hurricane will strike.

Weather satellites in space take pictures of the earth's atmosphere. Scientists can see how the clouds are forming.

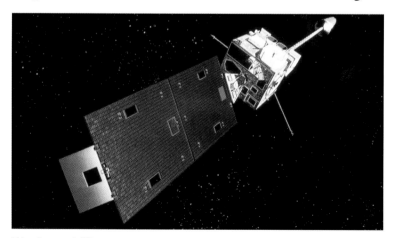

Weather satellite   National Weather Service

 29

Who tracks the hurricanes?

The National Hurricane Center in Coral Gables, Florida, tracks storms from the very beginning. They use satellite photos and radar.

When the low pressure system gets stronger, the center sends out a plane. Scientists with the *National Oceanic and Atmospheric Administration* fly a WP-3 plane right into the storm. It has a long pole, or probe, on its nose. The probe gets instant data on the pressure and humidity inside the hurricane. That helps scientists figure out how strong the hurricane is.

Navy hurricane-hunting planes
fly directly into the storms.

U.S. Navy photograph

The data is fed into the computers at the center. This helps forecasters. They decide when and where the hurricane might hit. Then they can issue warnings. This helps people prepare.

What happens once the National Hurricane Center decides a hurricane is coming?

First, the National Hurricane Center names the hurricane. Names make it easier to track different hurricanes. Men's and women's names are used. The lists are made up for five years in advance.

Then the National Hurricane Center issues bulletins to news media. Radio and TV stations are alerted.

There are two kinds of bulletins. A *hurricane watch* means that a specific part of a coast has a 50 percent chance of a hurricane striking it within 36 hours. Residents know they need to make plans to evacuate.

A *hurricane warning* means that a specific area is in danger almost right away. People must take action to protect life and property.

A hurricane can do great damage more than 100 miles from the center of the storm. So a large area can be involved.

Preparing for a hurricane is expensive and a lot of work. Storm shutters should be closed. Windows should be boarded up. Any loose objects must be tied down. All pets must be indoors. Boats must be moved from harbors.

People need to find a place to ride out the storm. They need to stock food that will last without refrigeration. They must have water, emergency lighting, firewood, and batteries for radios and TVs.

This may seem like a lot of trouble. But it's important for saving lives. The number of hurricane-related deaths has dropped since 1940. Only three times since then have more than 500 people died in a hurricane.

HURRICANE EVACUATION ROUTE

But property damage has gone up. From 1925–1929, hurricanes caused less than $400 million in damage. But from 1965–1969, the cost of damage rose to $2 billion! Then in 1992, Hurricane Andrew alone caused *$25 billion* in damages.

The federal government helps pay for the damage and cleanup. So hurricane damage means a big cost to taxpayers.

And costs will only rise in the future. More and more expensive buildings and houses are being built in coastal areas.

People need to think about where they're building. They need to think about how they're building. There are ways to build a house that can last in some hurricanes.

For example, Habitat for Humanity houses in Florida all survived Hurricane Andrew. No one was left homeless.

But 80,000 other homes were destroyed. What was the difference? Habitat for Humanity houses were built with care.

The Federal Emergency Management Agency (FEMA) issued some rules that Habitat for Humanity followed. These rules included having storm shutters and a low-pitched roof. Bolts and anchors were to be used in the frame. And the house was to be bolted to the foundation.

It's tragic that some builders cheat homeowners. They don't use enough structural support when building. They won't use proper materials. You can imagine what happens to poorly built houses in a hurricane.

What terror awaits people who don't evacuate? What does a hurricane really do? The next chapter relates true stories of hurricane horror.

National Hurricane Center

HURRICANE HORROR

What causes all this tragedy?

East Pakistan—500,000 dead. Bangladesh—250,000 killed. India—300,000 dead. The numbers make people gasp. Hundreds of thousands homeless. Property damage in the billions.

What causes all this tragedy? It's the horror of the hurricane. Throughout history, hurricanes are remembered for their devastation.

What happened to Jean Lafitte?

Jean Lafitte, the famous pirate, terrorized the Caribbean in the early 1800s. He had headquarters on the tiny island of Galveston, off the Texas coast.

What happened to him? Who or what ended his reign of terror?

He wasn't defeated by brave sailors. A hurricane wiped him out.

In 1818, a hurricane raged over the island. It leveled Lafitte's town and many ships. The hurricane destroyed his weapons and food supply. He was never able to regain his power.

 33

What happened in Galveston in 1900?

Another hurricane tore through Galveston in 1900. The weather bureau thought it would hit Florida. No one expected it to hit Galveston.

People weren't ready. They picnicked on the beach. They played in the raging surf. They laughed at the huge waves that picked them up.

The weather bureau sent out a man to warn the people. But they laughed at him.

Before long, the winds got stronger. Deck chairs overturned. Umbrellas turned inside out and flew away.

By this time, some people began to leave. As they got into their buggies to drive away, tiles flew off roofs and hit them. People began to panic.

But the waves raced faster than horses could run. Rain poured down. Winds whipped through the city. Water covered the bridges to the mainland. People were trapped on the island.

U.S. Weather Bureau

By evening, 110-mph winds battered the city. The winds drove 20-foot waves over the island. The raging waters broke into houses. The houses were destroyed.

People were killed. Debris battered them. They drowned. And they suffocated.

Uprooted trees and parts of buildings flew through the streets. People were dragged under the dark water. The survivors spent a terrifying night holding on to debris in the raging water.

The next morning, there was ruin everywhere. Smashed houses, telephone poles, dead animals, and thousands of

Hurricane winds drove a ten-foot-long board into the trunk of a palm tree.

human corpses clogged the streets. Bodies dangled from trees 20 feet high. Other bodies were stacked with piles of debris. The hurricane leveled half the town. At least 6,000 died.

The survivors thought they were saved. They thought all was well. But they didn't realize what awaited them.

They had no water, no food, no medical supplies, and no dry clothing. And there was no way out. The bridges were down. The boats were destroyed. The hurricane had done its work.

What happened in New England in 1938?

In 1938, a hurricane raged through New England. It was unexpected and powerful. It wiped out part of Long Island, New York. It hit Rhode Island too.

People haven't forgotten this hurricane. There was no warning. On Long Island, people had been at the beach, having a good time. The surf seemed a bit rougher than usual. Then the wind began to blow harder. So people began to leave. Many of them never reached home.

Two hours later, huge 30- to 40-foot waves hit the beach. The surge powered its way toward the middle of the island. The waves swept 50 homes into the sea.

That was just the beginning. High tension wires popped and fizzled in the water. One man was electrocuted.

An 18-year-old girl's car stalled in several feet of water. She was killed when a brick wall fell onto her car.

In Rhode Island, tragedy struck again. The hurricane hit as school was dismissing. One school bus was washed off into the waters as it started over a flooded causeway. A father had seen the bus coming and tried to stop the driver. But the driver didn't see the father's warning.

The waves washed over the bus. The driver opened the door. Children scrambled onto the roof. As the bus floated

away, the children held hands. Then the bus sank. Only one child was saved. But it wasn't the son of the man who tried to warn the driver.

One Long Island survivor thought a huge fog bank was rolling in. But it wasn't fog. It was a 40-foot wall of water. The storm surge did its work.

The Long Island hurricane wiped out 26,000 cars and 29,000 miles of electric and telephone wires. Nearly 1,000 people died. The hurricane also destroyed several thousand homes. Hundreds of millions of dollars were lost.

What happened during Hurricane Camille in 1969?

In 1969, Hurricane Camille ravaged Mississippi and Louisiana. Camille was a force-five hurricane, the most deadly. It was the most destructive storm to hit the U.S. mainland in history at that time.

The National Hurricane Center forecasted storm surges of 20 feet. Everyone was told to evacuate.

But in Pass Christian, Mississippi, some people stayed. Some wanted to have a "hurricane party." On the third floor of an apartment complex, 12 people began to party. They were still there when the water flattened the complex to the ground. Waves as high as a three-story house crushed it.

Pass Christian was the hardest hit. Camille destroyed nearly all the beachfront buildings. It tore through the rest of the town. It sucked four children out of their father's arms. They were flung into the howling wind. They were never seen again.

In Mississippi and Louisiana, 139 people died. But Camille wasn't finished.

Two days later, Camille dumped 30 inches of rain in 6 hours. Mud slides buried homes. Another 109 people died.

Hurricane Camille did help, though. Because of the horror,

 36

people began to take warnings more seriously.

Other hurricanes hit in the following years. Hugo ripped through Puerto Rico in 1989. Hugo drowned Puerto Rico with 2 ½ billion tons of water.

In 1991, 140-mph hurricane winds leveled Bangladesh. Waves almost 23 feet high slammed into the coast. More than 250,000 people died. About 10 million people were left homeless.

Warnings were given. But many people didn't have TVs or radios. They didn't hear about the hurricanes until they hit. And those who heard the warnings didn't believe them. There had been too many false alarms.

National Oceanographic and Atmospheric Administration

What happened during Hurricane Andrew in 1992?

Andrew was one of the most devastating hurricanes in history. When it hit Florida, nearly a million people fled. About 200 people died.

Andrew was the costliest hurricane to hit the U.S. mainland. The bill was 35 billion dollars!

But it could have been worse. If Andrew had traveled 20 miles farther north and stayed on that track, the damage would have been 100 billion dollars!

Andrew was a force-four hurricane. It had 145-mph winds, with gusts up to 175 mph. Its storm surge was 16 feet, a Florida record. It tore across Florida, leaving a 35-mile-wide path of destruction.

Most of the damage was done to buildings less than 20 years old. People had built without thinking of hurricanes. Wood-frame houses with peaked roofs were popular. People lived in trailers. They had built strip malls. Andrew leveled them all.

The winds even blew down the National Hurricane Center's radar. This huge radar crashed eight stories down on the South Dixie Highway. Forecasters had no more radar pictures of the storm.

Electricity went out, so there was no TV information on the storm. By 4 a.m., the wind reached a frenzy in south Dade County. The next morning, people staggered from their houses. They saw the damage.

Debris lay everywhere. Glass crunched underfoot. Windows were blown out. Roofs had blown off. The winds had sucked furniture out of homes.

Trees were gone. The landscape was bare. No one could drive. Fallen trees lay everywhere in the roads.

Stadium bleachers had blown into a highway. Semitrailers were on their sides. Sailboats lay in streets. Live fish swam in flooded parking lots. The pier was smashed.

Damage from
Hurricane Andrew
Bettman Archives

Some people were lucky. One family hid in a closet for hours. The roof blew off their house. Then the door blew out. The son was torn out of his mother's arms.

The mother ran screaming after her child through the hole where the door had been. Her husband chased after her.

They found their son. He had blown into a bush. The couple fought their way back to the remains of their house. Their child was safe.

Not everyone was so lucky. One woman had prepared. She had bought hurricane shutters. And she had enough water and food to last through the hurricane.

But Andrew shattered her house. The shutters held but the roof blew off. The walls collapsed on top of her. Her body was found two days later.

Two weeks passed before electricity was restored. No power meant no air conditioning. No trees meant no shade. And it was 90 degrees in Miami in the daytime.

Two hundred and fifty thousand people were left homeless. There was no ice or food. People drank warm soda. They ate dry cereal without milk.

Weeks passed before relief efforts worked. The government made big mistakes when asking for help. The requests never got to the right people. Too much paperwork snarled the process.

And communication was a huge problem. People in other parts of the United States wanted to help. They sent food. They sent blankets. They sent money. But it didn't get where it was needed.

It was ten days after Andrew before soldiers and marines came. They put up tent cities and helped with supplies. They helped people clear driveways and pull fallen trees off streets.

Ready-to-eat meals from the military came shortly after. Medicine, food, water, baby formula, and diapers finally arrived.

 40

Six months later, the federal government filed a report written by the secretary of Housing and Urban Development. It read in part:

Neighborhood after neighborhood remains unrepaired. There are endless piles of debris. Social services are either closed or stretched to the limit. Shopping malls and retail centers are boarded up and empty. Homestead Air Force Base remains a tangled mess of twisted hangars, [and] flattened and empty homes.

Today, the cleanup from Andrew continues. What happens next? What can people do in the future? Will new hurricanes be even more deadly? What is ahead for us?

Damage from Hurricane Andrew   Animals Animals/Earth Scenes

 41

HURRICANES AHEAD

What about global warming?

Hurricane Andrew ravaged Florida in 1992. A month later, Hurricane Iniki ripped through the Hawaiian island of Kauai. Four hurricane-force storms raged through Guam. Hurricanes hit American Samoa.

The 1992 eastern Pacific hurricane season broke records. Twenty-seven tropical cyclones hit. Twenty-four named storms bore down on land. The National Weather Service even ran out of names.

What caused these horrible hurricanes? Some scientists think *global warming* is to blame. Some believe even more hurricanes may be coming in the future. What can we do?

Weather is important in our lives. So people worry about changes in our weather.

Growing crops depends on weather. Having enough food depends on weather. Where we live is often decided by the weather. Global warming could change these things drastically.

What is global warming? Imagine being cold. Then you wrap a blanket around yourself. You get warm. Why?

It's not because the blanket is warm. The blanket is room temperature. Your own body heat warms you up.

 42

Instead of your body heat escaping, the blanket traps it. You get warmer.

When it's cold, we dress in layers. All the layers trap warm air in between and keep us warm.

Global warming is the same idea. A "blanket" of gases surrounds the earth. The gases keep the earth's heat from escaping into outer space.

The earth receives heat from the sun. Our atmosphere lets the heat in. The earth absorbs some of the heat and reflects the rest.

We can't see this heat. It's called *infrared radiation*. The human body gives off infrared too.

The earth sends this infrared radiation back into the air. There the infrared hits the atmosphere.

The earth's atmosphere is made up of gases such as *carbon dioxide* and *methane*. They surround the earth. The atmosphere contains *chlorofluorocarbons* too.

The gases act like a huge blanket, holding the heat in. This is known as the *"greenhouse effect."*

Our earth needs some kind of blanket. Without our atmosphere, all the heat would escape. The earth would be zero degrees. All the oceans would freeze solid.

But too much of a blanket would be a big problem. None of the heat could escape. Then the earth's atmosphere would get too hot. This possibility is called *global warming*.

So why is global warming becoming such a problem?

What causes these greenhouse gases? Why are they increasing? It's the changes in our ways of living.

One "greenhouse gas" is carbon dioxide. People produce carbon dioxide in factories and by driving their automobiles.

The carbon dioxide levels on earth stayed the same for thousands of years. Then in the middle of the 1800s, these

levels began to grow. More people mean more industry. More industry means more carbon dioxide.

Another "greenhouse gas" is methane. Ancient *bacteria* make methane. These bacteria live in swamps. They also live in people's and animals' intestines.

So how does methane get into the air? One way is through rice paddies. More people grow rice now than ever before. The rice paddies are like swamps. More rice paddies mean more methane bubbling up into the atmosphere.

Methane is produced in animals' intestines. More people eat beef than ever before. So more ranchers raise cattle. More cows mean more methane gases released into the air.

Finally, termites give off methane too. People are burning the rain forests. Termites love to eat burned wood. With more burned wood to eat, the number of termites grows. The more termites there are, the more methane is produced.

Another greenhouse gas is chlorofluorocarbon. Chloroflourocarbons are released by refrigerators, air conditioners, and car coolants. It's hard to imagine life without these things. But they add to the problem of global warming.

What does global warming mean to hurricanes?

Scientists all over the world study global warming. They argue about it. They research it. They try to find ways to stop it.

It is agreed that global warming will affect our weather. A temperature rise of only 7 degrees in the next 40 years would be dangerous. The polar ice caps would begin to melt. The sea level could rise from 6 to 26 feet. Hundreds of square miles of coastal land would be flooded. Lives would change forever.

But scientists disagree about what global warming means to hurricanes. Hurricanes need warm, moist air to grow. Some think that warmer ocean temperatures mean more fuel for

 44

hurricanes. And with rising temperatures on earth, hurricanes have more places to develop.

Other scientists say that warmer temperatures won't cause hurricanes. Warmer air evaporates more water. That makes thicker clouds. Thicker clouds can block out sunlight. Then the oceans wouldn't get warm enough to feed a hurricane.

Scientists can't predict what global warming will mean to hurricanes. They just know there will be an effect. The many violent storms and hurricanes of recent years seem to be a sign.

When do hurricanes form?

Scientists know that weather comes in cycles. Hurricanes usually form in certain months of the year. An old sailor's rhyme tells us.

> JUNE: too soon
> JULY: stand by
> AUGUST: you must
> SEPTEMBER: remember
> OCTOBER: all over.

August and September are peak hurricane months. From 1886–1990, the Atlantic made 519 hurricanes. Sixty-six percent of those formed in August and September. Another 18 percent formed in October.

Is there some way to destroy or control hurricanes?

Hurricanes cause untold damage. They kill. They ruin lives. Scientists keep hoping they can find a way to control a hurricane.

First, scientists thought possibly they could destroy a hurricane. But a hurricane is thousands of times more powerful

45

Hurricane Felix, August 10, 1995 National Weather Service

than an atomic bomb. So how could it be destroyed?

Then scientists wondered if they could steer a hurricane. But a hurricane bobs like a cork in a rushing river. And the winds steering a hurricane are extremely forceful. They are too strong for humans to control.

Steering a hurricane away from land would save lives. But it would also keep needed rain off crops.

Finally, scientists hoped they could weaken a hurricane. One famous idea was "seeding" a hurricane.

The strongest hurricanes have the smallest eyes. The bigger the eye, the wider the area the winds have to circle. So the wider the area, the slower the winds blow. Therefore, scientists thought that if they made the eye bigger, the wind speed would drop.

 **46**

Think of an ice skater. When she puts her arms in, she spins really fast. To slow down, she spreads her arms out.

So scientists considered cloud seeding to slow hurricanes down. They would drop *silver iodide* by airplane into a hurricane's eye wall. The silver iodide would make the water droplets freeze quicker. They would release their heat or energy. Then, like the arms of a skater, the eye wall would move outward.

But no one could tell for sure what might happen. Some scientists worried that the hurricane's eye would move back and forth between its old and new sizes. That might create an even worse hurricane.

Or what if a seeded hurricane veered away from the U.S. and into another country? The other country would be furious. The damage could be deadly.

Still, scientists decided to try. The experiment was called *"Project Stormfury."*

From the beginning, Project Stormfury had its problems. Scientists knew it was chancy, at best. But the newspapers tried to make it into a "hurricane-killer" project. This caused problems for the scientists, who knew they couldn't kill hurricanes.

During Hurricane Esther (1961) and Hurricane Beulah (1963), scientists tried seeding. But it was difficult to decide what the cloud seeding had really done.

Would the hurricanes have been worse without the seeding? There was no way to tell with Esther. But Hurricane Beulah's eye wall did grow. And the wind speeds dropped from 89 to 80 mph.

So scientists were hopeful. They got more money from the government and waited for another hurricane.

They knew they had to make just the right choice. First, the storm had to be a big one. That way, when it got smaller, everyone could tell.

 **47**

It also had to be a "typical" hurricane. Scientists had to be able to tell what it would have been like without the seeding.

Also, the chosen hurricane would have to develop far away from land. Then if scientists seeded it and it got bigger by accident, it wouldn't hit the United States.

Hurricane Debbie was seeded in 1969. Reaction was mixed. The wind speed dropped by 30 percent. But then the winds picked up the next day.

Still, scientists were happy. They had done something. They wanted to try again. But no more storms appeared.

And because results weren't firm, the public thought Project Stormfury was a mistake. So the government chose not to spend the taxpayers' money on the project anymore.

Scientists also considered towing icebergs into the oceans to weaken hurricanes. Hurricanes need warm water. So why not cool down the ocean?

This plan had too many problems. It would cost $15 million a year to tow icebergs into the hurricane latitudes. And it might cause other problems with the weather along the way. And how could you know when to start bringing the iceberg down?

Not only that, most hurricanes bring needed rain. If we stopped rainfall, crops wouldn't grow.

Another idea for weakening hurricanes was to cover the warm ocean with a layer of film. The film would stop the evaporation of water vapor. Then the hurricane would have no fuel.

This wasn't a workable idea for many reasons. The cost of covering an ocean would be too high. The hurricane's winds might whip up the film off the water. And how would you pick up the film once it was down? Also, it could cause many problems for the ocean life.

For now, scientists are still thinking. They're doing many experiments. But so far, no one has come up with an answer to controlling hurricanes.

There are too many factors involved. There are too many things that could go wrong. Hurricanes are just too powerful.

So what can we do about these killer storms?

At the very least, we should be able to tell when a hurricane is coming. But even this is difficult.

From 1944–1960, 15 huge hurricanes hit the East Coast. Then from 1970–1988, only two reached land. Why is this so? What makes hurricanes happen in some years and not in others?

Scientists don't fully understand these cycles. But one scientist is gaining ground.

Dr. William Gray of Colorado State University has convinced other scientists with his hurricane forecasting. Renowned hurricane expert Neil Frank says, "No one was capable of long-term hurricane forecasting at all before Gray came along."

Dr. Gray has been forecasting hurricanes for the last 11 years. He's been on target every time but twice.

Dr. Gray uses many factors. One thing he considers is the amount of rainfall in West Africa. When West Africa has a drought, there are few hurricanes. When West Africa has a lot of rain, there are many hurricanes.

He also looks at the easterly wind strength. He checks the warmth of the eastern Pacific Ocean. Dr. Gray uses many computers and a complex mathematical formula to forecast.

Many scientists knew about all these factors. But Dr. Gray "was the first to link these things together," says Robert Sheets, director of the National Hurricane Center in Florida.

Dr. Gray and other scientists are afraid the cycle of relatively few hurricanes is about to change. West Africa has had a drought for 25–30 years. During those years, there were few hurricanes.

 **49**

On June 17, Hurricane Agnes was causing heavy rain in Cuba.   NOAA

By June 19, hurricane Agnes was over Florida, and storm   NOAA
clouds extended as far as Virginia.

Now there is a lot of rain in West Africa. And the number of hurricanes has increased.

Dr. Gray thinks the government should fund more hurricane research. "In this century," he says, "hurricanes have killed 10 times the number of people as have earthquakes. They've done about 4½ times more damage. But the federal government spends 4 or 5 times more for earthquake research than for

 50

hurricane research. If we see a return of major storms and get one or two a year like Andrew," Dr. Gray adds, "it's just going to be disastrous."

Dr. Bruce Rosendahl of the University of Miami believes we are in for being "battered senseless" by hurricanes in the future.

What are the most recent advances for predicting hurricanes?

Today, scientists use many new advances to predict hurricanes. One is *Doppler radar*. It bounces sound off the clouds in the hurricane. Then it can measure the wind speed.

Scientists also use satellites and weather stations. Still, the only way to get real data about a hurricane is to fly right into it.

But the major problem faced by hurricane forecasters is the hurricane itself. The many factors involved make hurricanes difficult to predict.

A hurricane can suck up a burst of energy just before landfall. It can explode like a bomb.

Or it can limp ashore and then fade away. Then people who have gathered supplies and boarded up their houses feel they have wasted their time.

It's expensive to evacuate too. It costs approximately one million dollars to evacuate one mile of shoreline.

And what if the hurricane misses an area it's predicted to hit? The next time those people hear a hurricane forecast, they might not believe it. And that's exactly when it might hit.

With a hurricane, you never know for sure. So you have to be prepared for the worst.

Glossary

bacteria	a tiny, one-celled, living organism that often causes disease.
Beaufort Scale	a measurement scale showing the effects of wind speed.
carbon dioxide	a colorless, odorless gas made naturally when people breathe out, when something is burned, or when plant matter decays.
chlorofluorocarbons	a compound made of carbon, hydrogen, chlorine, and fluorine that was once used as a refrigerant (for refrigerators and freezers) or for aerosol sprays.
condensation	a process that occurs when a liquid is removed from a vapor.
convection cells	a huge pocket filled with air that is always moving or rotating because hot air rises and cold air sinks.
Coriolis effect	changes in movement of wind patterns caused by the spinning of the earth.
cyclones	what hurricanes (violent, rotating windstorms) are called in the Indian Ocean.
Doppler radar	a weather measuring device that can bounce sound off clouds or rain. It can measure wind speed.

equator	a division of the earth around its center, dividing it into northern and southern halves.
"eye" of the hurricane	the center of the violent storm about 10–30 miles across, where calmer weather is found.
eye wall	the band of rain and winds surrounding the eye of the hurricane.
global warming	the warming of the earth's atmosphere caused by gases that trap heat and don't allow it to be reflected back into the atmosphere.
greenhouse effect	the result of global warming—when heat is trapped by gases.
greenhouse gas	any gas that traps heat close to the earth and doesn't allow it to escape.
high pressure area	an area in the atmosphere where cold air is sinking toward the earth.
hurricane	a violent, rotating windstorm with winds over 74 mph.
hurricane warning	a warning issued by the National Hurricane Center weather authorities that a specific part of a coast is in danger almost right away. People should evacuate.
hurricane watch	a notice given by the National Hurricane Center weather authorities that a specific part of the coast has a 50 percent chance of a hurricane striking it within 36 hours. People should make plans to evacuate.

infrared radiation	invisible heat from the sun or from hot objects radiated back into the atmosphere.
low pressure area	an area in the atmosphere where warm air is rising.
meteorologists	scientists who study weather and weather conditions.
methane	an odorless, colorless natural gas made by bacteria that live with no oxygen. Methane is given off by decaying plant and animal matter.
National Hurricane Center	national government center in Coral Gables, Florida, for studying hurricanes.
National Oceanic and Atmospheric Administration	(NOAA) national agency studying weather and oceans.
northern hemisphere	the top half of the earth, above the equator.
Project Stormfury	a project designed by scientists to try to control hurricane strength.
rain bands	lines of intense rain clouds and high winds that circle the hurricane.
Saffir-Simpson scale	a scale for measuring hurricanes that includes barometric pressure, storm surge, wind speed, and damage index. It was designed by the head of the National Hurricane Center and an engineer.

 54

silver iodide	a powder used to make water droplets freeze quickly, thus releasing their heat, or energy.
southern hemisphere	the southern half of the earth, below the equator.
storm surge	ocean whipped up to huge heights by hurricane winds.
3^2	three times three = nine.
tropical depression	a tropical cyclone with winds of up to 38 mph.
tropical storm	a storm with winds of 39–73 mph.
tsunamis	rising waters caused by a geologic event such as an earthquake or volcanic eruption.
2^2	two times two = four.
typhoons	the name for hurricane-force winds in the Pacific Ocean coming from the Chinese word "taifeng."
updrafts	upward currents of warm, rising air.
water vapor	a mix of air with tiny water droplets, like fog or mist.
whirlpool	a rapid, rotating movement, as in water or winds.

Index